The Greatest Epic of All Time

MAHABHARATA

Sterling Publishers Private Limited
A-59, Okhla Indl. Area, Phase II, New Delhi 20
Tel: 91-11-26386165; Fax: 91-11-26383788
E-mail: sterlingpublishers@airtelmail.in
Website: www.sterlingpublishers.com

Printed at Sterling Publishers Pvt. Ltd, New Delhi

Preface

'Mahabharata' literally means 'the great story of the Bharat dynasty'. Divided into 18 *parvas* or books, it is one of the longest epic poems in the world with more than 74,000 verses and long prose passages.

The *Mahabharata* was dictated by Vyasa and written by Lord Ganesha. Ganesha is said to have agreed to write it only on the condition that Vyasa never pause in his dictation, and Vyasa agreed on the condition that Ganesha took the time to understand the content before he took it down.

The *Mahabharata* claims, *"What is found here, may be found elsewhere. What is not found here, will not be found elsewhere."*

It narrates tales of ambition and intrigue in royal courts, renunciation and a final battle in which the good triumph over the wicked. The epic unfolds the dynastic struggle between the Pandavas and the Kauravas for the throne of Hastinapura, the kingdom ruled by the Kuru clan. The struggle culminates in the great battle of Kurukshetra, in which the Pandavas were ultimately victorious. The epic ends with the death of Krishna and the subsequent end of his dynasty, and the ascent of the Pandavas and Draupadi to heaven.

Besides compelling drama, the *Mahabharata* has characters that are larger than life – Krishna, shown as an incarnation of Lord Vishnu, Bhishma, the grandsire of all principal warriors, Yudhishthira, the son of Dharma, compelled to lie to win the battle, Arjuna, the unparalleled archer, Duryodhana, driven to disaster by overarching ambitions. Yet a sense of reality is maintained, with each character making the *Mahabharata* a fascinating read.

As a part of history, the epic is of immense importance to Hindu culture. It has attracted tremendous attention and interest from philosophers, litterateurs, and laypersons, not only in India but all over the world.

The stories of *the Mahabharata* exemplify the underlying discussion of the four human goals: *artha* (purpose), *kama* (pleasure), *dharma* (duty) and *moksha* (liberation). They offer pearls of wisdom strung into a beautiful and coherent treatise on every aspect of the ideals of life and living, the true meaning of duty and sacrifice, happiness and sorrow. The inner kernel of the *Mahabharata* continues to remain relevant. Therein lies its greatness, its sacredness.

Over the ages, the *Mahabharata* has been looked upon as the epic relating the complicated sequence of events leading up to a battle of humongous proportions and the human and moral casualties thereof. The war of Kurukshetra has also been known as *Dharmayuddha* or the 'War for Righteousness'. This epic also contains the Geeta—Krishna's instruction to Arjuna as to what constitutes *dharma (righteousness)*.

A multi-coloured panorama of characters and emotions, and the ongoing struggle between black and white, between the straight and narrow, and the twisted and subversive, and especially between those who have the knowledge of the righteous action and the rare few who have the courage of conviction to put it into practice.

Finally, as Krishna said, "The battle for right conducted through physical force, leads to numerous wrongs and, in the net result, *adharma* increases."

In ancient Hastinapura, there was a king named Shantanu of the Kuru dynasty. He had three valiant sons. Bhishma, the eldest, vowed never to marry. Chitrangada was martyred in a battle. His brother Vichitravirya had two sons, Pandu and Dhritarashtra. Though the elder, the visually challenged Dhritarashtra could not become king, and so his brother Pandu ascended to the throne. Pandu had five sons whom the people called the Pandavas, while Dhritarashtra had a hundred sons and one daughter who were together known as the Kauravas. The Kauravas, headed by the eldest, Duryodhana, were forever at loggerheads with the more popular, valiant and honest Pandavas. As his brother Pandu died, Dhritarashtra ascended to the throne as a regent for prince Yudhishthira who was too young to rule.

Duryodhana wanted to be declared heir-apparent, but, as Yudhishthira was the eldest among the cousins, and more popular, Dhritarashtra could not favour his own son.

But Duryodhana was not the kind to give in so easily. He said, "In that case, send the Pandavas to Varanavata for one year, while I try to win the love of the people."

After Duryodhana left, the king wondered what his son's plan was. But he loved his son blindly, and decided to let him have his way. So he sent for the Pandavas. When the Pandavas came, Dhritarashtra said, "I think you all need a change as you have been in Hastinapura for a long time. Why don't all of you go to Varanavata, along with your mother, for a while?"

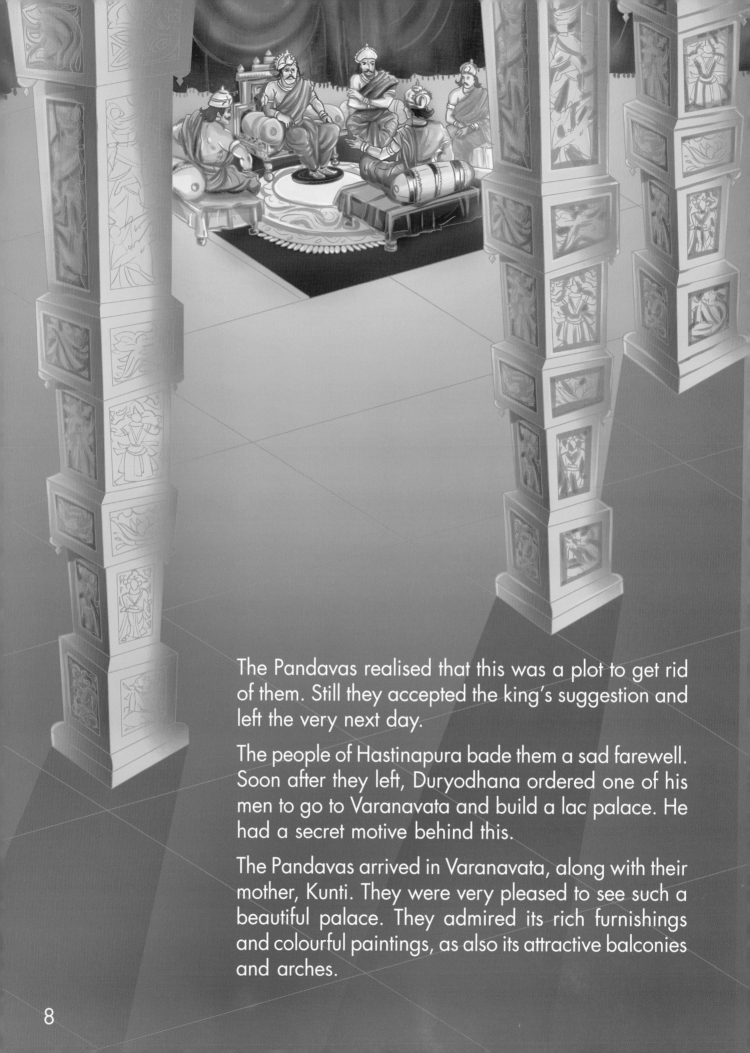

The Pandavas realised that this was a plot to get rid of them. Still they accepted the king's suggestion and left the very next day.

The people of Hastinapura bade them a sad farewell. Soon after they left, Duryodhana ordered one of his men to go to Varanavata and build a lac palace. He had a secret motive behind this.

The Pandavas arrived in Varanavata, along with their mother, Kunti. They were very pleased to see such a beautiful palace. They admired its rich furnishings and colourful paintings, as also its attractive balconies and arches.

The Pandavas soon settled down in their new palace. One day, their uncle Vidura sent a messenger.

"Your uncle Vidura has sent me to dig a tunnel from this palace to the banks of the river," the man said. "In case of any danger, you must escape by that route."

Bhima asked, "Why will we have to escape?"

The man explained, "This palace was made of lac by the orders of prince Duryodhana. The guard is to set fire to it as soon as he receives orders to do so."

The man immediately began digging the tunnel. A year passed, but the guard was not ordered to set fire to the palace. Always on the alert, the Pandavas became very impatient. Arjuna suggested that they themselves set fire to the palace and escape unhurt. All the others agreed with his plan. But they decided not to return to Hastinapura.

So, one dark night, the Pandavas set fire to the palace and escaped through the tunnel.

They moved through the darkness till they reached the banks of the river. There, they were met by a boatman sent by Vidura.

The boatman rowed them across to the other side of the river. Then, the Pandavas disappeared into the thick forest that bordered the river.

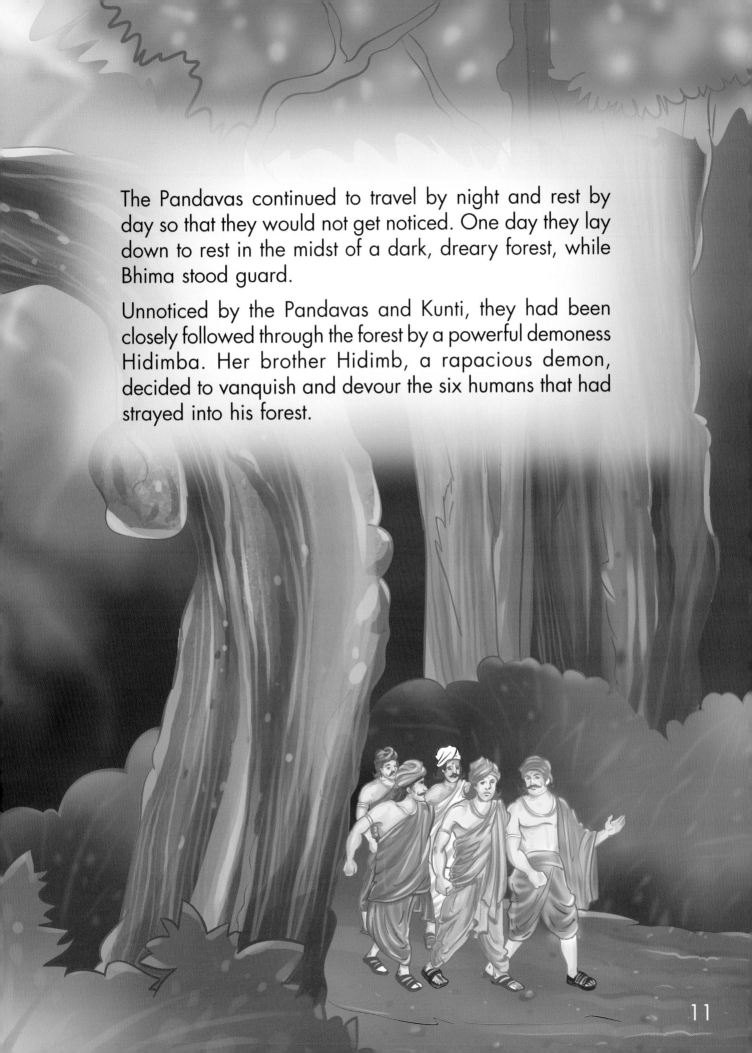

The Pandavas continued to travel by night and rest by day so that they would not get noticed. One day they lay down to rest in the midst of a dark, dreary forest, while Bhima stood guard.

Unnoticed by the Pandavas and Kunti, they had been closely followed through the forest by a powerful demoness Hidimba. Her brother Hidimb, a rapacious demon, decided to vanquish and devour the six humans that had strayed into his forest.

Hidimba approached the sleeping Pandavas as a beautiful woman and warned the watchful Bhima of the evil designs of her brother. Enraged, Bhima challenged the demon and killed him in a fierce fight that made the earth tremble.

Hidimba's love for Bhima resulted in their marriage, and then the birth of their mighty and obedient son Ghatotkacha. The Pandavas decided to quit this itinerant life and settled as brahmins in a potter's house in Ekachakra.

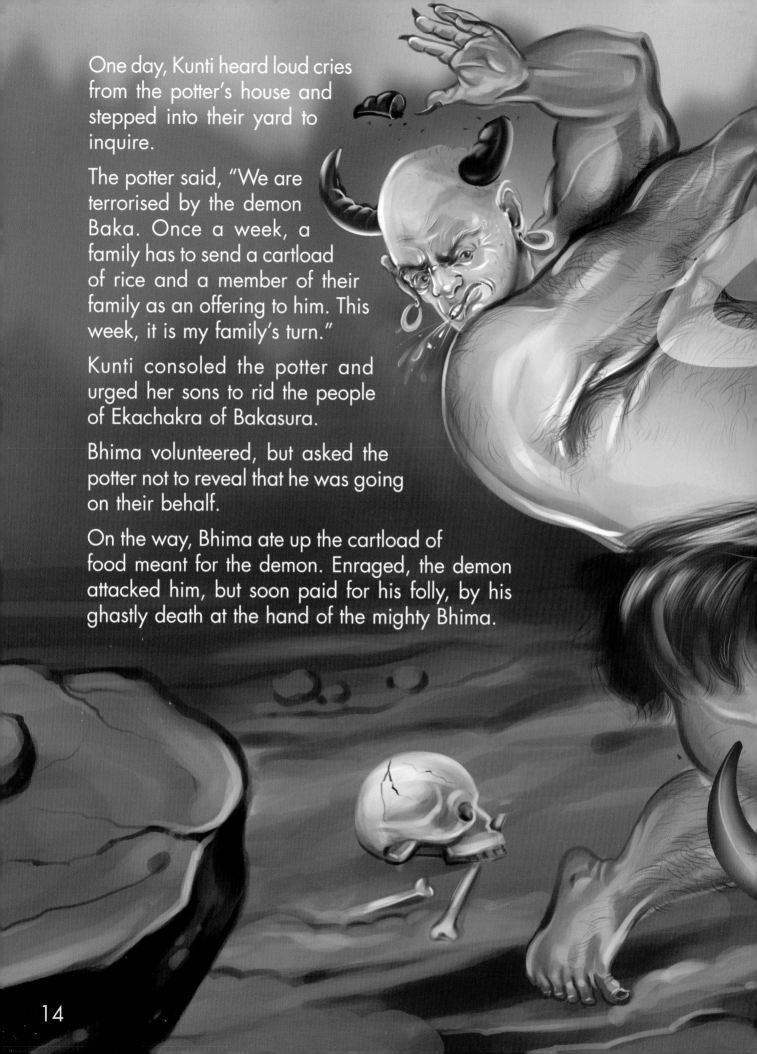

One day, Kunti heard loud cries from the potter's house and stepped into their yard to inquire.

The potter said, "We are terrorised by the demon Baka. Once a week, a family has to send a cartload of rice and a member of their family as an offering to him. This week, it is my family's turn."

Kunti consoled the potter and urged her sons to rid the people of Ekachakra of Bakasura.

Bhima volunteered, but asked the potter not to reveal that he was going on their behalf.

On the way, Bhima ate up the cartload of food meant for the demon. Enraged, the demon attacked him, but soon paid for his folly, by his ghastly death at the hand of the mighty Bhima.

14

Then one day Bhima came to Arjuna and said, "King Drupada of Panchala has announced that he is holding a *swayamvara* for his daughter Draupadi. It will be a test in archery and the winner will marry the princess. You should definitely try your luck!"

A *swayamvara* is an event in which the princess garlands the suitor she choses to marry.

"How is it possible? We have not been invited to the *swayamvara*!" said Arjuna. "I wonder if I should go."

"Yes, you should go. You are one of the best archers. You will surely win the contest!" said Yudhishthira.

The Pandavas disguised themselves as poor brahmins and went to Panchala. When they reached the court of king Drupada, they saw the many kings and princes present there. The brothers quietly slipped into the great hall and sat among the common people.

King Drupada sat on his throne with princess Draupadi beside him. She had a garland in her hands.

A mighty bow was kept in the hall. The king explained, "Whoever strings this bow and shoots an arrow through the eye of the golden fish revolving at high speed will win my daughter's hand in marriage. But the contestants must do so by looking at the reflection of the fish in the water and not where the fish is placed – directly overhead on the ceiling."

All the kings and princes tried to string the mighty bow. But alas! Most of them could not even lift it! And those who did manage to lift and string it, failed to hit the target. Thus none of them were successful. Then, Karna, the son of the Sun god stepped forward. He picked up the bow with ease and hit the target accurately. But Draupadi refused to marry a man of low caste.

Then Arjuna, disguised as a poor brahmin, asked for permission to try his skill.

When the king assented, Arjuna picked up the bow and strung it with ease. After that, he knelt down in front of the water, took aim and shot the fish through the centre of its eye.

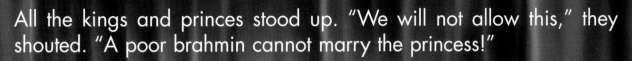

All the kings and princes stood up. "We will not allow this," they shouted. "A poor brahmin cannot marry the princess!"

They quickly drew out their swords, but King Drupada calmed them down, saying, "This man has won the contest. So he shall marry my daughter."

Draupadi quickly put the garland around Arjuna's neck and left her father's palace.

When the Pandavas, along with Draupadi, reached their home, Kunti was somewhere inside the house.

Jokingly, they called out to their mother, "Mother, come and see what we got in our begging bowl today."

Kunti, without looking up, gave her typical response, "Whatever it is, be sure to share it amongst yourselves."

"What did you say, Mother?" asked Yudhishthira.

"I said, share whatever you have brought, as you have always done," Kunti replied.

The brothers looked confused. Their mother's word was law!

And so, Draupadi became the wife of the five Pandavas!

"Oh dear! What have I done?" cried Kunti when she saw Draupadi. "Why didn't I look before I uttered those words? What can be done now?"

When King Drupada heard about this, he protested, but to no avail.

The fact that the Pandavas were alive became known far and wide. Duryodhana's spies told him that the Pandavas had become rich as well, being the sons-in-law of King Drupada.

Duryodhana was disappointed because his plans had failed.

His friend Karna was also enraged as he had been rejected by Draupadi at the *swayamvara*, in favour of his arch-enemy, Arjuna.

23

In anger, Karna said, "We should attack the Pandavas at once!"

Duryodhana agreed to this.

"Don't be silly," Bhishma, the grandsire said. "Your army will not be able to defeat the Pandavas because King Drupada is on their side."

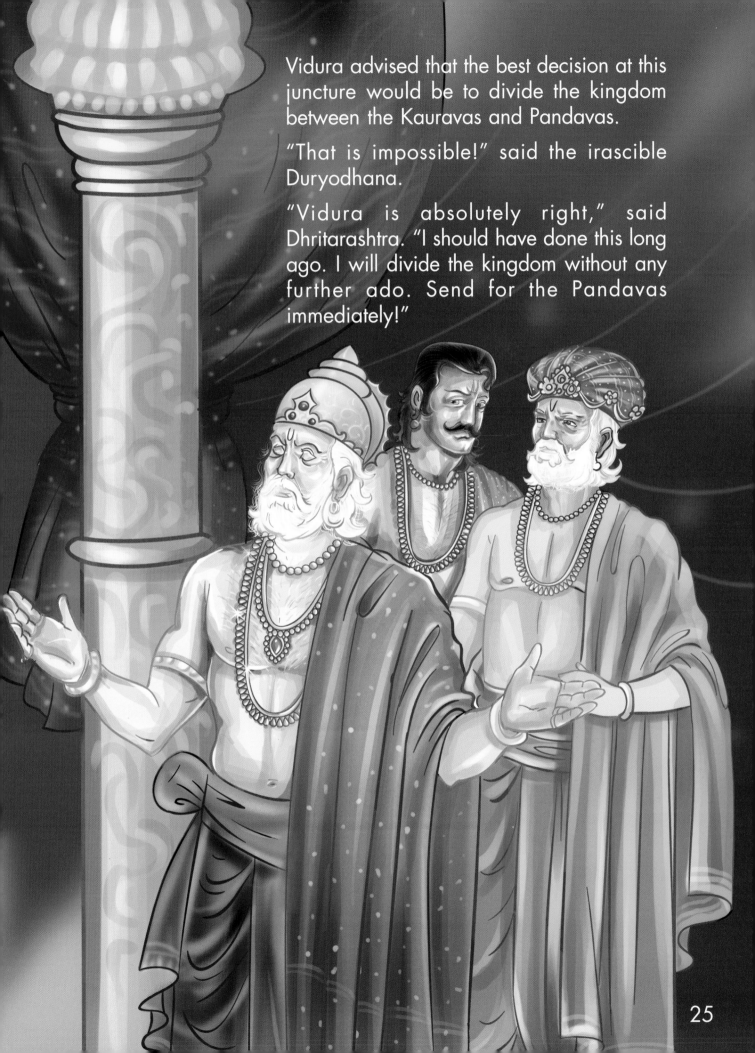

Vidura advised that the best decision at this juncture would be to divide the kingdom between the Kauravas and Pandavas.

"That is impossible!" said the irascible Duryodhana.

"Vidura is absolutely right," said Dhritarashtra. "I should have done this long ago. I will divide the kingdom without any further ado. Send for the Pandavas immediately!"

The Pandavas arrived in Hastinapura with Kunti, Draupadi and their cousin, Krishna. Krishna was the king of the Yadavas and a steadfast friend of the Pandavas.

People rejoiced as soon as their chariots were espied and they were welcomed with great fanfare.

The Pandavas went straight to Dhritarashtra.

After the customary formalities, Dhritarashtra apprised the Pandavas of his decision to divide the kingdom. Hastinapura was to be ruled by Duryodhana, while Yudhishthira was to be crowned the king of Khandavaprastha.

Outwardly, Yudhishthira and the other Pandava brothers accepted Dhritarashtras's decision with grace. But they felt the division was unfair because Khandavaprastha was rocky and barren like a desert!

Soon Yudhishthira left for his kingdom with his brothers, mother and Draupadi. Krishna also accompanied them.

Arjuna was furious. He said, "What an unjust division! I will not let you accept this, brother. What is the use of this desert? We will not live here!"

"He is right. I don't want to live here," added Bhima.

Yudhishthira tried to reason with his brothers. "We have to stay here because uncle has made me the king of this kingdom. After all, who are we to judge our elders?"

"If the elders are wrong, they should be questioned!" said Arjuna and Bhima together.

Krishna, who had been listening to the brothers all along, tried to console them. He said, "Yudhishthira is right! So what if this is desert land? We will work hard and turn it into a beautiful kingdom!"

The work began. The Pandavas and Krishna's workers worked day and night. Very soon the city grew into a glorious kingdom!

Krishna renamed Khandavaprastha as 'Indraprastha' because it was as beautiful as Indra's city in heaven. The fame of the kingdom spread far and wide, and people thronged to it. Small rulers of neighbouring areas paid rich monetary tributes to Yudhishthira for his patronage and friendship. The kingdom soon grew prosperous.

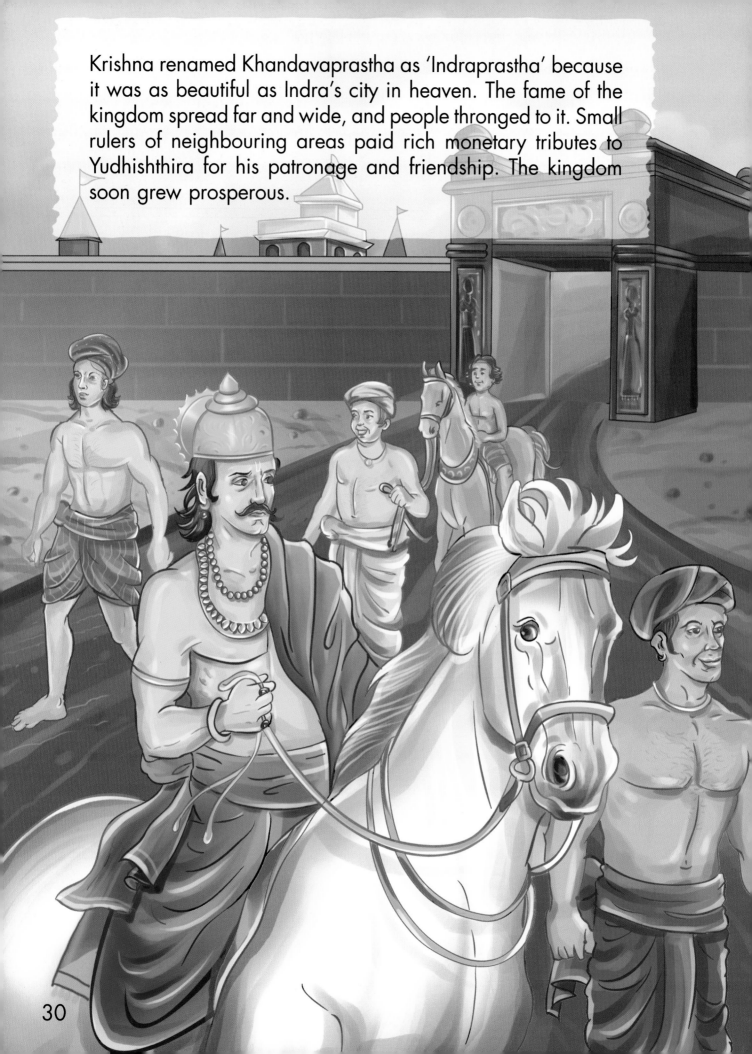

Indraprastha's fame drove Duryodhana mad with jealousy. In order to see how true the rumours were, he decided to visit the kingdom himself.

Palatial buildings and colourful gardens dotted either side of the roads. The palace of the Pandavas was the grandest. Wherever Duryodhana went, he found that people were wealthy, happy and content.

A few days after Duryodhana returned from Indraprastha, his uncle, Shakuni, came to see him.

"Uncle, we have failed to destroy the Pandavas in the past. But this time we must not fail!"

"That is not easy, Duryodhana," Shakuni reminded him. "The Pandavas are powerful opponents."

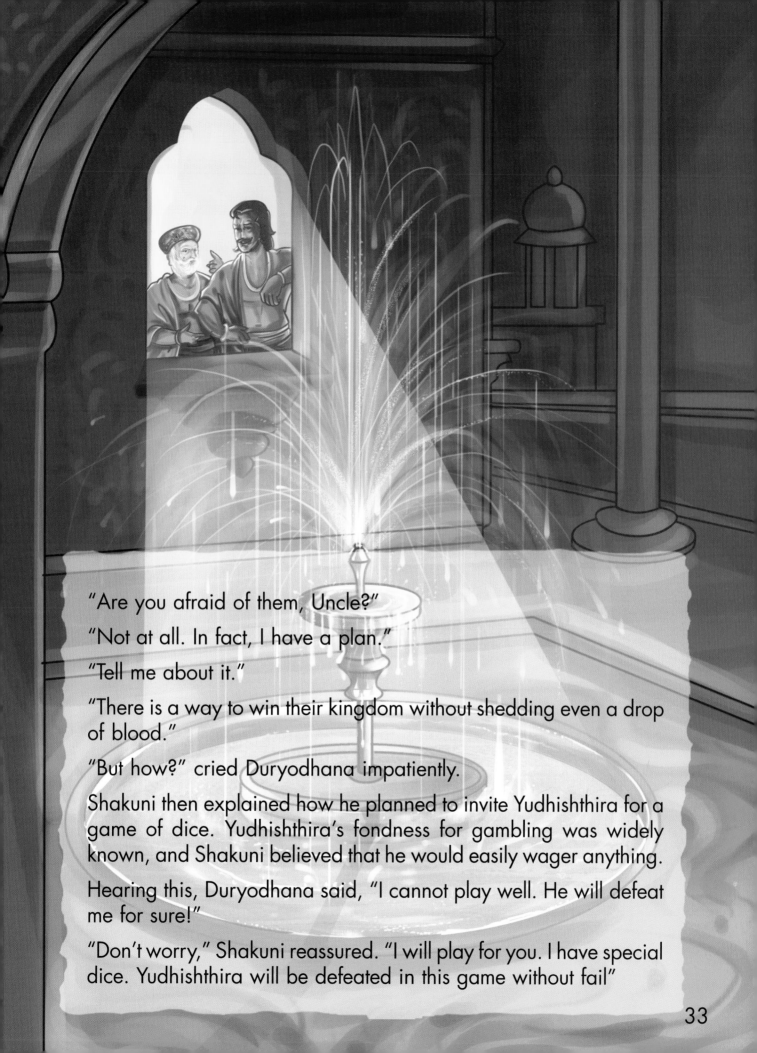

"Are you afraid of them, Uncle?"

"Not at all. In fact, I have a plan."

"Tell me about it."

"There is a way to win their kingdom without shedding even a drop of blood."

"But how?" cried Duryodhana impatiently.

Shakuni then explained how he planned to invite Yudhishthira for a game of dice. Yudhishthira's fondness for gambling was widely known, and Shakuni believed that he would easily wager anything.

Hearing this, Duryodhana said, "I cannot play well. He will defeat me for sure!"

"Don't worry," Shakuni reassured. "I will play for you. I have special dice. Yudhishthira will be defeated in this game without fail"

"What if Yudhishthira refuses to play with you?" asked Duryodhana.

"He will not refuse. I will ensure that," replied Shakuni.

Duryodhana was very pleased with his uncle's plan.

A few days later, Duryodhana went to his father and told him that he wanted to invite the Pandavas to Hastinapura as they hadn't visited them for a long time. Delighted, Dhritarashtra readily agreed.

Duryodhana said, "I want to play a game of dice with Yudhishthira because he is a good player."

Dhritarashtra had a feeling that Duryodhana was plotting against Yudhishthira. But, on inquiry, Duryodhana denied it.

A messenger was sent and the Pandavas came with him. Kunti and Draupadi also accompanied them.

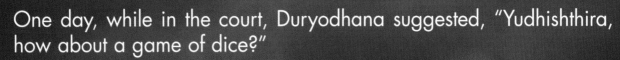

One day, while in the court, Duryodhana suggested, "Yudhishthira, how about a game of dice?"

"I don't play any more. It is an evil practice," said Yudhishthira

"I think you are afraid of losing," Shakuni said.

"I am not. I could play one game to prove it," said Yudhishthira. "Duryodhana, come. Let us play."

"My uncle Shakuni will play on my behalf," said Duryodhana.

"No one can play on anyone's behalf. Each one must play for himself!" said Yudhishthira.

"You are just looking for excuses because you don't wish to play," Duryodhana laughed at him.

Yudhishthira knew Shakuni would cheat. But there was nothing he could do. So, he agreed to play.

Everyone came together to watch the game when it began.

"My wealth against yours. Do you agree?" Duryodhana asked. Yudhishthira agreed.

The dice rolled and Yudhishthira lost his wealth.

'Never mind,' he thought. 'What if I have lost my wealth, I still have other possessions.'

He continued playing. Shakuni threw his dice deceitfully and Yudhishthira lost again — he lost his horses, chariots, servants and soldiers.

"Now what will you bet, Yudhishthira?" asked Shakuni.

"Bet your kingdom against mine," suggested Duryodhana.

"That is not right," shouted Bhima. "You cannot win or lose a kingdom by rolling a dice!"

But Yudhishthira disregarded Bhima's words and accepted the stake. Shakuni cast the dice and took away with it Yudhishthira's kingdom.

"I have won the kingdom of Indraprastha!" cried a gleeful Duryodhana.

Shakuni mocked Yudhishthira and told him to bet his brothers.

With the loss of his wealth and kingdom, Yudhishthira seemed to have lost his senses too. He went along with the terrible suggestion and ending up losing his brothers as well! After that, he pledged himself. Again he lost!

"Now what will you bet?" laughed Shakuni.

"He has Draupadi. You can place her at stake, Yudhishthira," scoffed Duryodhana.

"Are you out of your mind, Duryodhana?" screamed Vidura. "Do not involve Draupadi in this!"

"Stay out of this, Uncle. This is between us and the Pandavas!" said Duryodhana.

Yudhishthira agreed, much to the chagrin of his brothers. Shakuni rolled the dice, and Yudhishthira lost Draupadi! Everyone in the court was shocked into silence.

Duryodhana too sat quietly for a while and then said, "I will give you one more chance. If you win, you will get back everything you have lost. But if you lose, you will be exiled for twelve years. In the thirteenth year, you will have to stay hidden from everyone, and if you are discovered during that year, you will be exiled for yet another twelve years. However, if you succeed in staying hidden for that one year, you will get back your kingdom. Do you agree?"

Yudhishthira had no other option but to agree. He decided to play one more game. But alas! He lost again!

Duryodhana, now the ruler of two kingdoms, ordered the Pandavas to remove their expensive clothing, jewellery, etc., as all of it now belonged to him.

"Bring Draupadi here. She now belongs to us!" he said.

"Duryodhana, don't you dare insult Draupadi!" warned Bhima.

But Duryodhana made it clear to him that Bhima was his slave now, and slaves could not raise their voice. He then asked his brother, Duhshasana, to bring the beautiful and proud Draupadi to court.

Duhshasana went to Draupadi and said, "Your husband has lost you in the game of dice. You now belong to Duryodhana!"

"I don't believe you," said Draupadi.

"Come to the court, then you will believe me."

"I will not come."

"If you dare refuse, I will drag you to the court."

"No, you will not!"

This made Duhshasana very angry. He caught her by her hair, and dragged her into the court.

Draupadi cried and begged to be told that all that was happening around her was untrue. But everyone present in the court, including the Pandavas, hung their heads in shame and did not answer.

Duryodhana shouted, "Duhshasana, disrobe her!"

"Don't you dare touch her!" roared Bhima.

"Draupadi, if your husbands cannot protect you, come sit in my lap and be mine," jeered Duryodhana.

At this, Bhima took a terrible oath of killing Duryodhana by breaking his thighs.

"Duhshasana, do as I tell you," Duryodhana screamed. Duhshasana caught hold of her sari and began to strip it off her. Draupadi fell on her knees and cried, "Help! Krishna, help me!"

Duryodhana laughed cruelly while Draupadi continued to chant, 'Krishna-Krishna'.

The people present in the court gaped at Duhshasana. The more he pulled the sari, the longer it became. Drops of perspiration fell from his forehead. It seemed as if Draupadi was wrapped in unending yards of regalia. The gathering was stunned to see the miracle. Finally, Duhshasana gave up and sat down.

Not a soul moved for a while. Then Bhima thundered, "Duhshasana, you have sinned! For this, I will rip your chest and drink your life blood from it!"

Sensing the enormity of what Bhima had said, Dhritarashtra tried to mend matters, but in vain.

Completely shaken, the Pandavas, along with Draupadi, went into exile.

When King Drupada and Krishna heard about the Pandava's exile, they came visiting to console them and offer their support.

Krishna promised Draupadi that the Kauravas would pay for their misdeed.

Meanwhile, far away in Hastinapura, Duryodhana could just not rest. The Pandavas were on his mind all the time. Day and night, he only thought of killing the Pandavas.

When the twelfth year was nearly over, the Pandava brothers began to plan for the thirteenth year that would be the most difficult and trying of all.

King Virata, the ruler of Matsya, was a very noble man. He was loved by his people. King Virata's wife, Sudeshna, had a brother called Kichaka, who was the commander-in-chief of the Matsya army. He was a very strong and cruel person. The Pandavas decided to spend their thirteenth year, in disguise, in the kingdom of Matsya.

Everyone was pleased with their new identities, and all went well. They passed eleven months without hindrance. The Pandavas lived and worked in Matsya, and no one recognised them. But in the twelfth month, Draupadi got into trouble. Kichaka, the queen's brother saw Draupadi and fell in love with her.

Draupadi was then asked to serve Kichaka as well. She refused, saying, "I have five husbands, and they would be very angry if they got to know that I was being forced to serve Kichaka!" But the queen and the king held no sway over Kichaka.

When Bhima came to know of this, he was very furious. So, one night, when he got an opportunity, he killed Kichaka!

The news of Kichaka's death spread like wildfire.

Far away in Hastinapura, Duryodhana heard about Kichaka's death and screamed in frustration.

"Kichaka was a very strong man. Only Bhima is powerful enough to kill him," cried Duryodhana. "This means that Bhima is in Virata's palace, and so are the other Pandavas!"

The Kauravas decided to attack the kingdom of Virata without further ado. This would force the Pandavas to come out of hiding and participate in the battle. And as the thirteenth year of exile was not yet over, they would have to return to the forest for another twelve years.

Within a few days, Duryodhana led his army into King Virata's kingdom. Pandemonium struck Virata's capital. Bhima heard about the preparations for the battle and rushed to the king.

He said, "Please give me permission to come with you."

"But you are merely a cook," answered Virata.

"I am not a cook," said Bhima. "I am Bhima."

"Then come with me to join the army. But wait! Where are your brothers?"

"There is Yudhishthira," said Bhima pointing towards one of the ministers standing nearby. "And there are Nakula and Sahadeva," he said, pointing to the stableboys.

The king was puzzled. Soon, a woman came riding a chariot.

"What is the dance teacher, doing here?" asked the king, surprised.

"That is Arjuna," replied Bhima.

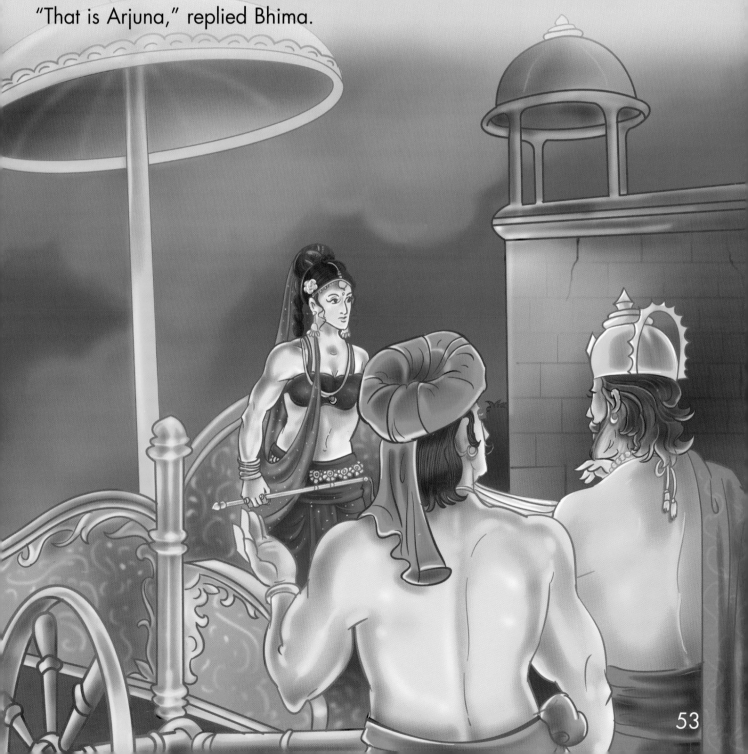

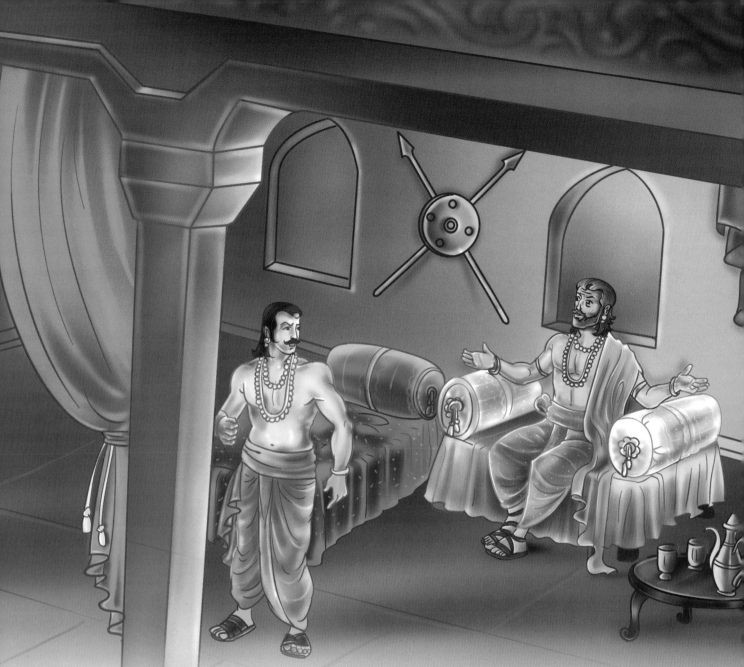

King Virata's army, along with the Pandavas, fought the war.

Dronacharya, Duryodhana and Karna led the army from the other side. The moment Duryodhana recognised Arjuna, he was thrilled.

"It was foolish of Arjuna to have come!" said Duryodhana. "The Pandavas will have to return to the forest now, as he has been recognised by us before the thirteenth year is over."

"I am afraid, Duryodhana," said Dronacharya, "the thirteeth year got over a few days ago."

Dronacharya was one of the greatest archers in the world. He had tutored the Kauravas and the Pandavas. Duryodhana was very upset with the information and asked Karna to attack Virata's army immediately!

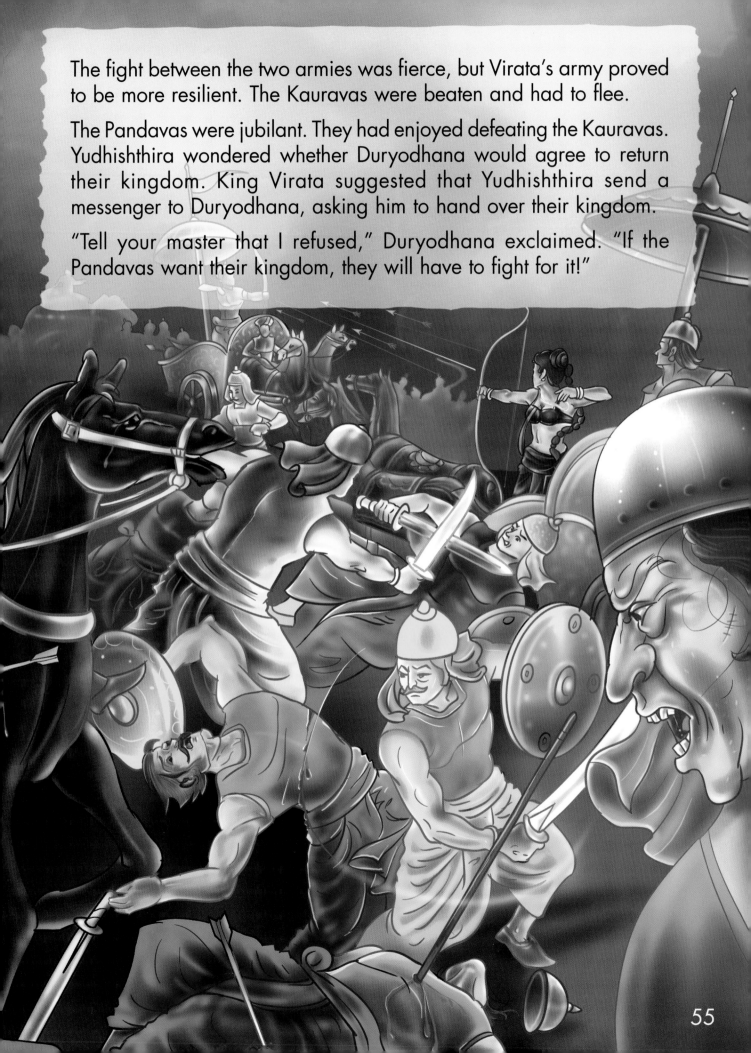

The fight between the two armies was fierce, but Virata's army proved to be more resilient. The Kauravas were beaten and had to flee.

The Pandavas were jubilant. They had enjoyed defeating the Kauravas. Yudhishthira wondered whether Duryodhana would agree to return their kingdom. King Virata suggested that Yudhishthira send a messenger to Duryodhana, asking him to hand over their kingdom.

"Tell your master that I refused," Duryodhana exclaimed. "If the Pandavas want their kingdom, they will have to fight for it!"

55

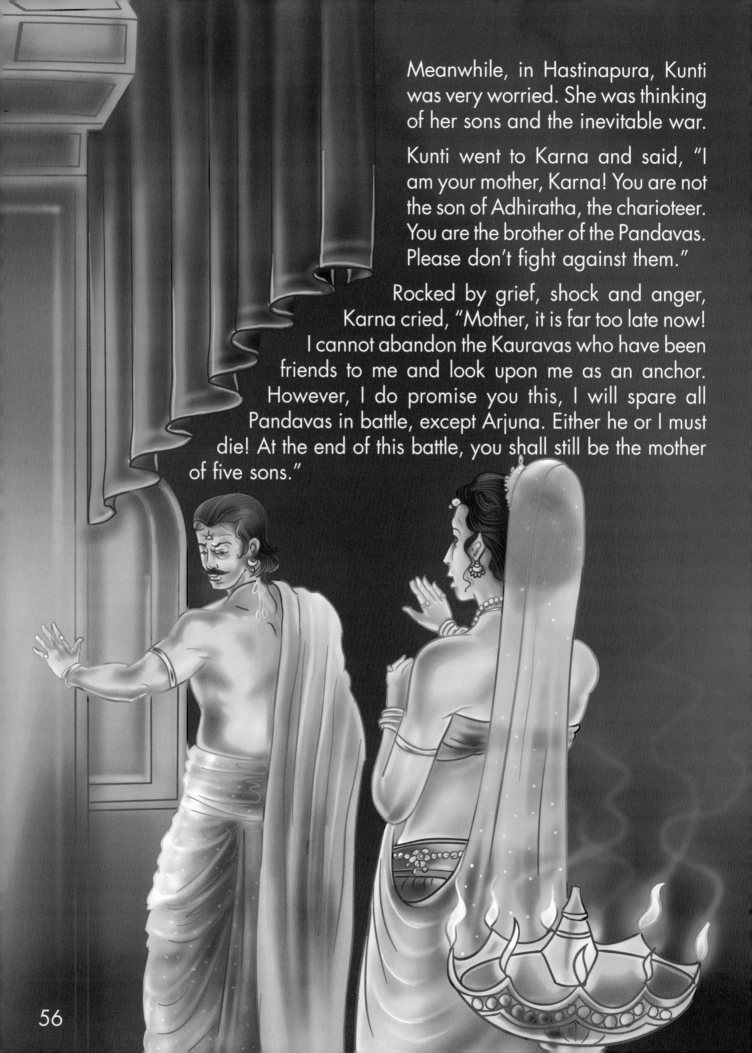

Meanwhile, in Hastinapura, Kunti was very worried. She was thinking of her sons and the inevitable war.

Kunti went to Karna and said, "I am your mother, Karna! You are not the son of Adhiratha, the charioteer. You are the brother of the Pandavas. Please don't fight against them."

Rocked by grief, shock and anger, Karna cried, "Mother, it is far too late now! I cannot abandon the Kauravas who have been friends to me and look upon me as an anchor. However, I do promise you this, I will spare all Pandavas in battle, except Arjuna. Either he or I must die! At the end of this battle, you shall still be the mother of five sons."

Kunti wept when she heard Karna, but she could do nothing and blessed her son before he walked away.

The Pandavas were very disappointed with Duryodhana's reply. They wanted peace, not war. They sent word to all the princes who were likely to join them, in case a war broke out. The Pandavas decided that Arjuna should go to Krishna immediately and ask for his support. At once, Arjuna left for Dwaraka to meet Krishna.

57

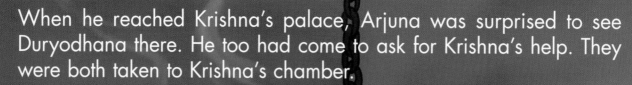

When he reached Krishna's palace, Arjuna was surprised to see Duryodhana there. He too had come to ask for Krishna's help. They were both taken to Krishna's chamber.

Krishna was sleeping on his sandalwood bed. A beautiful throne stood near the head of his bed and a golden cloth was spread out near his feet. Duryodhana went straight to the throne and sat down. Arjuna sat near the foot of his bed. They both waited in silence. When Krishna woke up, his eyes fell on Arjuna who stood in front of him and he extended a warm welcome.

Duryodhana said, "I came here first, so I should get first preference!"

"You came to see me first," Krishna told Duryodhana, "but I saw Arjuna first."

Nevertheless, being fair to both, Krishna said that one of them could take his army, and the other could take him. But he would only drive a chariot as he had made up his mind not to fight in the war. Duryodhana was allowed to make his choice first.

"I choose the army," said Duryodhana without any hesitation.

Arjuna, on the other hand, was happy that Krishna would be on his side.

Both returned satisfied. Duryodhana was delighted to have extra men on his side during the war, and Arjuna was elated that Krishna had agreed to be by his side.

The day of the battle was fast approaching. All the preparations were made. Bhishma, the grandsire was chosen as the chief commander of the Kaurava force. Karna did not approve of this decision. Bhisma did not appreciate the appointment of Karna as a high rank officer, and Karna refused to fight under his leadership. Draupadi's brother, Dhrishtadyumna, was chosen as the chief of the Pandava army.

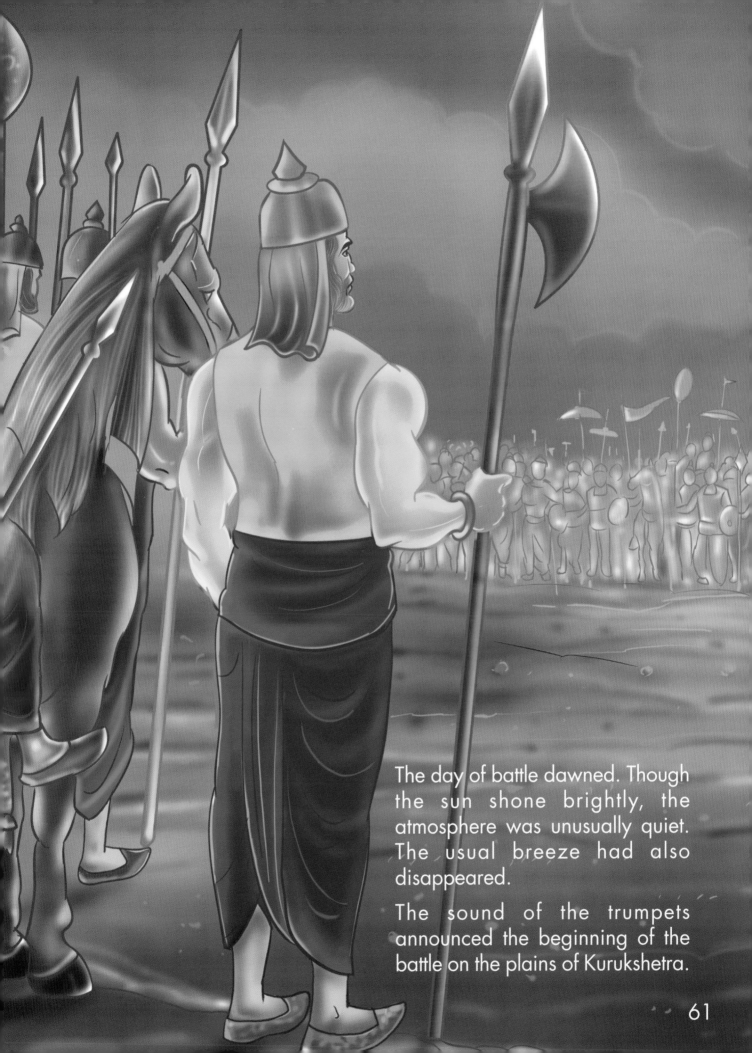

The day of battle dawned. Though the sun shone brightly, the atmosphere was unusually quiet. The usual breeze had also disappeared.

The sound of the trumpets announced the beginning of the battle on the plains of Kurukshetra.

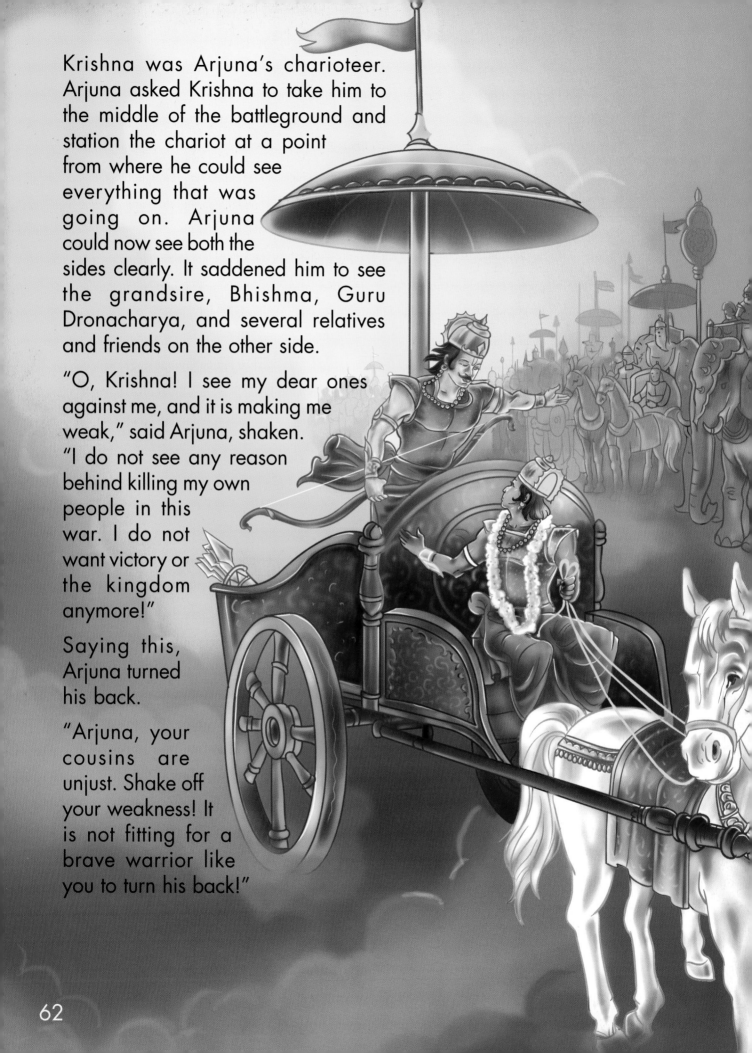

Krishna was Arjuna's charioteer. Arjuna asked Krishna to take him to the middle of the battleground and station the chariot at a point from where he could see everything that was going on. Arjuna could now see both the sides clearly. It saddened him to see the grandsire, Bhishma, Guru Dronacharya, and several relatives and friends on the other side.

"O, Krishna! I see my dear ones against me, and it is making me weak," said Arjuna, shaken. "I do not see any reason behind killing my own people in this war. I do not want victory or the kingdom anymore!"

Saying this, Arjuna turned his back.

"Arjuna, your cousins are unjust. Shake off your weakness! It is not fitting for a brave warrior like you to turn his back!"

But Arjuna would not see reason. Krishna then said, "You should perform your duty whenever and wherever it is required. The path of duty is superior for Ksatriyas. It is not right to leave any task incomplete."

Krishna further said, "Always keep in mind that you will have to fight for truth and justice at every step of your life. Even if you face your own people on the other side, you must fight. It is not important *who* you fight, but *what* you fight for!"

Arjuna was still hesitant. Eventually, Lord Krishna displayed his divine infinite form and revealed the eternal truth to him.

63

His face was completely surrounded with a glow. Then he said, "I am beyond time and limit. I am the birth, the beginning, the middle, and the end of everything. I am present in all things, and everything exists in me. So fight for what is right, selflessly, for you are only an object of destiny to get its act fulfilled."

Arjuna bowed his head and said, "Please forgive me for my ignorance. I am now ready for the war!"

Thus began the great battle of Kurukshetra. Elephants trumpeted and horses neighed. The armies clashed with each other in full fury. Swords flashed all around. The morning sky was covered with clouds of dust and the whole of Kurukshetra trembled with the sound of weapons.

On the first day, Abhimanyu, Arjuna's son, fought bravely, shooting arrows with great agility. Bhishma killed many men and all the Pandavas and Kauravas fought courageously.

Before the day got over, the battlefield was covered with bodies of soldiers who had sacrificed their lives. At sunset, the conch was blown, indicating the end of the day's battle.

The next day, Arjuna and Bhishma faced each other. They were equally matched. Arjuna was unwilling to harm the grandsire. So Bhishma's attacks caused great loss to the Pandava army.

By the end of the second day, Bhima and Dhristadyumna succeeded in defeating many opponents.

The battle between the cousins continued. Eight days passed. No matter how much they tried, Duryodhana's men could not defeat the Pandavas. Angry, Duryodhana went to Bhishma and accused him of protecting the Pandavas.

On the ninth day, Bhishma again faced Arjuna. But Arjuna was not convinced that Bhishma should be killed to end the war. Finally, Krishna got off the chariot and was about to fight Bhishma, when Arjuna pleaded with him to stop. He then agreed to fight Bhishma without any hesitation.

On the tenth day, Shikhandi accompanied Arjuna on his chariot. Born the prince of Panchala, Shikhandi had actually been Princess Amba in his former life and had vowed to avenge herself against Bhishma. Knowing her to be a woman, Bhishma refrained from attacking them.

Using Shikhandi as a shield, Arjuna attacked Bhishma and the valiant hero sunk to the ground with the arrows piercing his body forming a gruesome bed in the battlefield.

Everyone gathered around Bhishma in concern. When Karna learnt that Bhishma was wounded, he asked forgiveness for his past outbursts and ignorance. Bhishma forgave him, and asked everyone present there to return to the battlefield, as it was not yet time for him to make his journey to the heavenly abode.

Duryodhana asked Karna to become the commander of the army. But Karna felt that the position should have been offered to Dronacharya.

On the eleventh day, under the leadership of Dronacharya, the Kauravas caused heavy devastation in the Pandava army.

On the thirteenth day, Arjuna headed out in a different direction with Krishna as his charioteer. Taking advantage of the situation, Dronacharya arranged the army in the complex wheel formation. Yudhishthira was in a quandary as he realised that it would be impossible to defeat the Kauravas without breaking though the formation.

Arjuna's youthful and valiant son Abhimanyu knew how to break into the formation but not how to issue forth from it.

Finally, Yudhishthira asked Abhimanyu to break into the formation. Glowing with pride and valour, Abhimanyu pierced through the formation. However, the other generals of the Pandava army were prevented from entering the formation by Jayadratha, the King of Sindhus.

Alone inside the formation, the invincible Abhimanyu was treacherously attacked together by all the generals of the Kaurava army. His charioteer and horses were killed. Karna broke Abhimanyu's bow, and Drona, his sword. He was struck in his heart with an arrow as he wielded the wheel of his chariot to defend himself.

Abhimanyu's death was a big blow to the Pandavas. Yudhishthira blamed himself for Abhimanyu's death. The whole camp broke into tears.

When Arjuna and Krishna returned, there was absolute silence and the camp was in darkness. They rushed inside.

Arjuna found everyone in tears. Krishna inquired, "What has happened? Why are all of you crying?" Looking around, Arjuna asked, "Where is Abhimanyu? Where is my son?"

"I have killed your son, Arjuna," wailed Yudhishthira.

"What do you mean by that, brother?" asked Arjuna, in agony.

Yudhishthira narrated how the Kauravas had killed Abhimanyu and how the brave youth had to fight back all alone.

Arjuna's grief was uncontrollable. He was heartbroken. How would he face Abhimanyu's mother, Subhadra, and his wife, Uttara, who was expecting his child? Blinded by grief, Arjuna vowed, "Tomorrow before sunset, either I will kill Jayadratha or sacrifice myself!

The Kauravas rejoiced at Abhimanyu's death. They had thought that the Pandavas would lose heart and the battle would cease with their return to exile. The sudden twang of Arjuna's bow, and the bellow of Krishna's conch told the Kauravas that all had not gone as they had anticipated.

Duryodhana wondered why Abhimanyu's death had not engendered grief and panic in the Pandava's camp. Perceiving Duryodhana's concern, Dronacharya said, "Abhimanyu's death has made Arjuna furious."

Duryodhana's spies informed him of Arjuna's vow. Duryodhana was worried because he knew that Arjuna always fulfilled the vows he took.

He said, "We must help and protect Jayadratha at all cost. If Arjuna fails to kill Jayadratha, he would have to kill himself. With him gone, we would win the war."

"Duryodhana, do you think your army can kill Arjuna?" asked Dronacharya. "There is no one who can stop him."

Dronacharya's words angered Duryodhana. He fumed, "You never speak any encouraging words to us. You always favour the Pandavas. Why don't you leave us and join them?"

"I am the commander-in-chief. I would not leave your side even in the face of defeat," said Dronacharya and left the place, feeling very upset.

The next morning, a scared Jayadratha said to Duryodhana, "I am returning to my kingdom because I don't want to be killed by Arjuna!"

"Be brave, Jayadratha," said Duryodhana. "My best warriors will be beside you to protect you!"

There was great excitement in the battlefield that day. Dronacharya stood at the frontline of his army to stop the Pandavas from entering the Kaurava battle formation. Jayadratha remained at the back, protected by the Kaurava army.

Arjuna successfully defeated the soldiers in the first barricade and reached closer to where Jayadratha was, when Duryodhana challenged him. They fought fiercely. Duryodhana was protected by the divine armour that Dronacharya had given to him. So Arjuna aimed all his arrows towards those parts of Duryodhana's body which were not safeguarded by the armour.

Badly wounded, Duryodhana fled from the battlefield.

The sun was about to set, and Arjuna had been unable to find Jayadratha. The Pandavas became restless. They searched for him everywhere. Suddenly it became dark all around. Warriors of both armies cried, "The sun has set, the battle is over for today."

But Krishna told Arjuna that the sun had not actually set. He had only covered the sun with his Sudarshan Chakra. Jayadratha came out of his hideout as he thought the sun had set.

Krishna removed the chakra to reveal the sun.

Arjuna spotted the unguarded Jayadratha, and targeted an arrow which flew straight and hit Jayadratha's neck and separated it from the rest of the body. Arjuna twanged his bow and Krishna blew his conch and the entire field knew that Arjuna had fulfilled his vow.

The sun had set but the battle did not stop. It continued even through the night.

On the fourteenth day of the battle, the armies fought through the night. Ghatotkacha, Bhima's son with Hidimbi, joined the Pandava army. Endowed with supernatural powers, Ghatotkacha flew into the air and became stronger in the darkness. He caused such great panic and devastation in the Kaurava army that Karna had to use 'the spear of unerring effect' that he had saved to kill Arjuna. Ghatotkacha was vanquished and the Pandavas were bereaved again.

Dronacharya continued to decimate the Pandava army. As he was a great archer and could not be killed in fair fight, the Pandavas decided to trick him.

With his heavy iron mace, Bhima killed an elephant named Ashwatthama and proclaimed, "I have killed Ashwatthama!"

Dronacharya became anxious when he heard Bhima's words because his son's name was Ashwatthama!

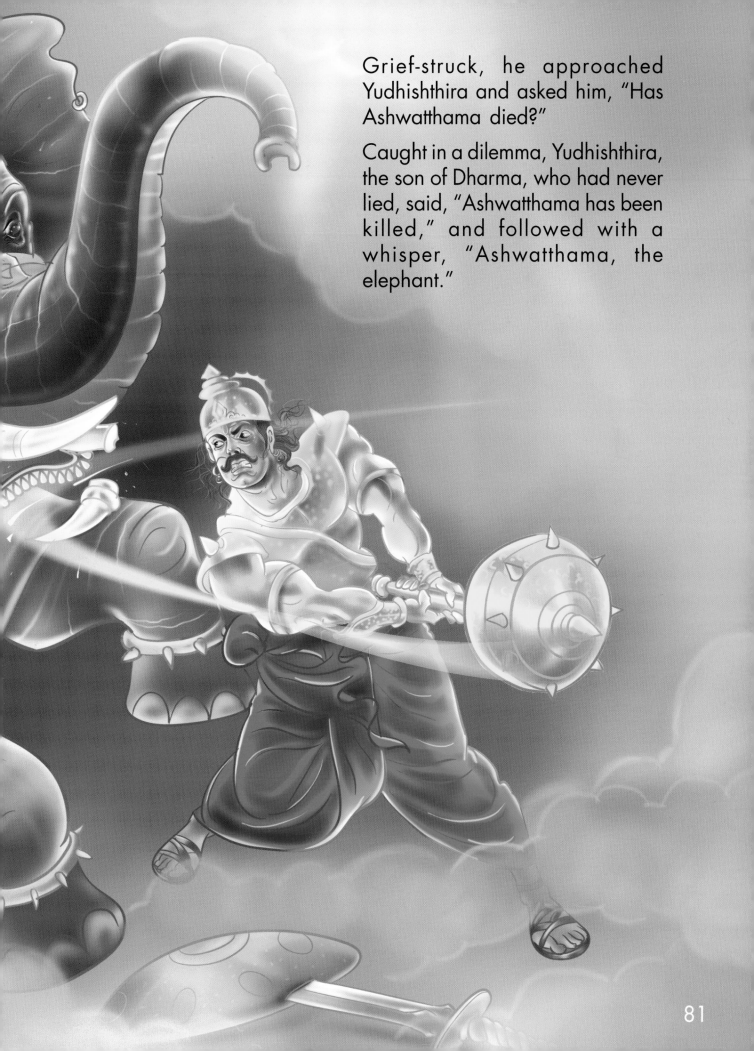

Grief-struck, he approached Yudhishthira and asked him, "Has Ashwatthama died?"

Caught in a dilemma, Yudhishthira, the son of Dharma, who had never lied, said, "Ashwatthama has been killed," and followed with a whisper, "Ashwatthama, the elephant."

Unable to hear the whisper in the uproar of the war, Dronacharya believed his son dead. Discarding his weapons, he sat in his chariot deadened with grief.

Taking advantage of the situation, Dhristadyumna beheaded him. Dronacharya's death was a great blow to the Kauravas.

Karna now became the commander of the Kaurava force.

On the fifteenth day of the battle, Bhima attacked Duhshasana. Years ago, when Duhshasana had attempted to disrobe Draupadi, Bhima had vowed to rip apart his chest and drink his blood. Bhima, the bull among men, fulfilled his vow and dealt another setback to the Kauravas.

Enraged by the death of Duhshasana, Karna fought Nakula and would have killed him, but let him go because of his promise to Kunti. Karna could have also killed Yudhishthira and Sahadeva, but spared them too.

On the sixteenth day, Arjuna and Karna finally came face to face.

Everyone in the battlefield waited with bated breath to watch the two iconic warriors in action. Even the gods descended to witness the clash of the titans. Karna aimed his weapons well and reapeatedly cut the string of Arjuna's bow. He shot an arrow which narrowly missed his opponent. Then his chariot wheel got stuck in the mud.

His charioteer, Shalya refused to get down to pull it out. Arjuna took aim but hesitated when he saw an unarmed Karna get off his chariot. He had never been unfair in war. Perceiving the hesitation, Karna appealed to Arjuna's sense of honour, "Is it fair to attack me when I'm defenseless?"

Outraged, Krishna said, "Is it fitting that you appeal to Arjuna's sense of fair play? Were you not present when Abhimanyu was killed defenseless? Was it fair when the Kauravas cheated Yudhishthira of his kingdom? Or when Draupadi was dragged to the court in front of you, and you jeered at her?"

Ashamed, Karna got into his chariot and shot back. But suddenly he felt that all his knowledge of weaponry and their use had deserted him. Arjuna raised his bow and took aim. His arrow flew swiftly and the valiant Karna lay dead on the battlefield.

Mourning the death of his noble son Karna, the sun set and there was darkness everywhere.

Aggrieved at the death of his brothers, relatives and friend, Karna, the dispirited Duryodhana walked away from the battlefield towards the pool of water.

In relentless pursuit, the Pandavas soon found him near a lake, and Yudhishthira asked, "Why are you hiding, Duryodhana?"

Duryodhana said that he no longer wanted his kingdom, Hastinapura. He had no desire to live, as most of his brothers were dead.

Yudhishthira urged Duryodhana to continue fighting and fulfil his duty as a Ksatriya. He also ensured fair play by deciding that Duryodhana would only duel with one Pandava at a time and not be set upon by the five together.

Bhima and Duryodhana engaged in a duel with maces. At Krishna's behest, Arjuna reminded Bhima of his oath of shattering Duryodhana's thighs by slapping his own. Duryodhana leapt in the air to attack Bhima, as Bhima's mace came down heavily on his thigh, and broke it irreparably.

Unable to bear the pain, Duryodhana sank to the ground. Yudhishthira appealed to Bhima to not kill Duryodhana, and the Pandavas left the battlefield with a heavy heart. Their triumph in battle was marked by the grief and solemnity of the death of brave warriors.

Ashwatthama sat beside the dying Duryodhana recounting all the wrongs committed in the battle by the Pandavas. Driven mad with grief, as the scenes of the death of his father, Karna and Duhshasana flashed past his mind's eye, Ashwatthama made the terrible oath of avenging their untimely death.

Late the same night, Ashwatthama entered the Pandava camp unnoticed and slew Dhrishtadyumna, and the five sons of Draupadi, all of whom were blissfully asleep.

The Pandavas, Krishna and Draupadi were saved because they were not present in the camp. When they discovered the cruel slaughter, Draupadi demanded that Ashwatthama be punished or she would sacrifice herself.

Aware that the war was over with the death of Duryodhana, the bitter Ashwatthama decided to annihilate earth. Before the Pandavas could look for him, he had turned a blade of grass into an unerring weapon and hurled it towards them. Once deflected, the weapon targeted the child in Uttara's womb, but Krishna assimilated it in himself. Ashwatthama left Kurukshetra and wandered into a forest.

Victorious in war, the Pandavas returned to Hastinapura. The people welcomed them with great fanfare. The Pandavas approached the desolate royal couple, Dhritarashtra and Gandhari, and begged to be forgiven for the death of their hundred sons and other relatives.

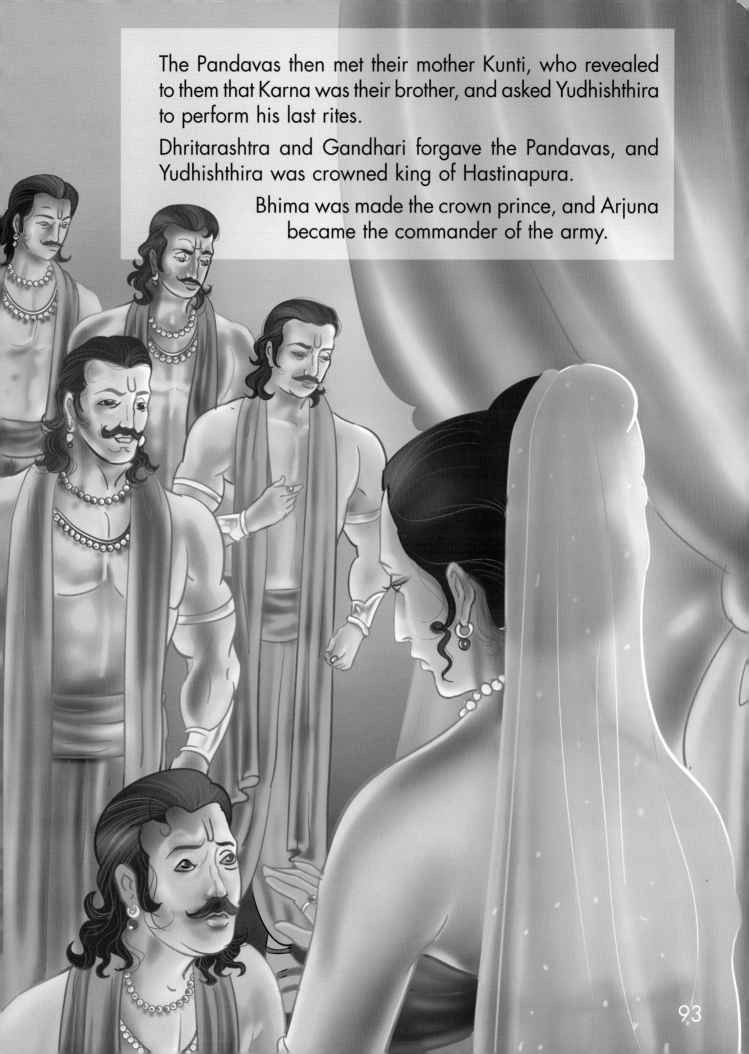

The Pandavas then met their mother Kunti, who revealed to them that Karna was their brother, and asked Yudhishthira to perform his last rites.

Dhritarashtra and Gandhari forgave the Pandavas, and Yudhishthira was crowned king of Hastinapura.

Bhima was made the crown prince, and Arjuna became the commander of the army.

After a few days, the Pandavas and Krishna went to pay their repects to Bhishma in Kurukshetra. He blessed them and then his soul left for its heavenly abode.

Yudhishthira ruled the kingdom with wisdom. He was a just king and everybody loved him.

Uttara gave birth to a baby boy, who was named Parikshit.

Dhritarashtra, Gandhari and Kunti lived for fifteen years with the Pandavas in Hastinapura. Then they left for a forest where they lived for three more years.

Then one day, their abode in the forest caught fire and they passed away.

Yudhishthira ruled Hastinapura for many years. When they grew old, the Pandavas decided to renounce the world and set off for Indralok. Yudhishthira crowned Parikshit, king of Hastinapura.

The Pandavas, along with Draupadi, faced many testing times on the way, but their sincerity helped them overcome every obstacle.

And so Yudhishthira finally entered heaven with Draupadi, and all his brothers, and found everlasting peace and happiness.

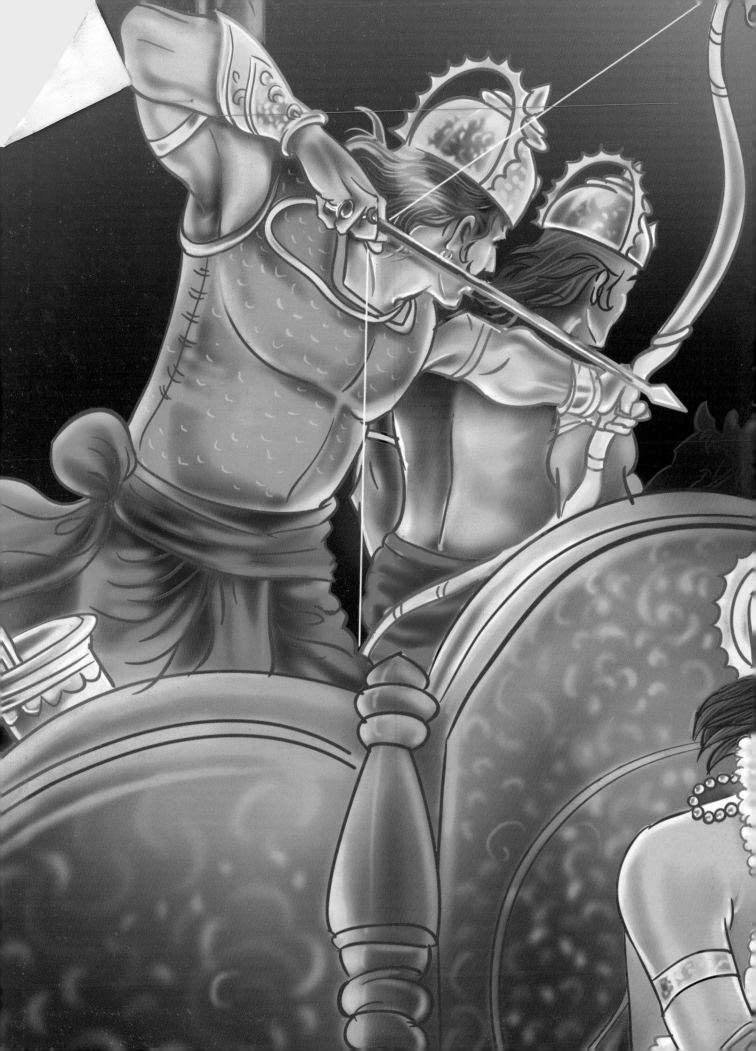